WILL POWER
and the Ten Commandments

By Magdalen Lindon
Illustrated by Tom Spooner

redemptorist
p u b l i c a t i o n s

Published by **Redemptorist Publications**

Alphonsus House, Chawton, Hampshire, GU34 3HQ, UK
Tel. +44 (0)1420 88222, Fax. +44 (0)1420 88805
Email rp@rpbooks.co.uk, www.rpbooks.co.uk

A registered charity limited by guarantee
Registered in England 3261721

Copyright © Redemptorist Publications 2018
First published November 2018

Text by Magdalen Lindon
Edited by Rachel Thompson
Designed by Peena Lad
Illustrated by Tom Spooner

ISBN 978-0-85231-541-5

A CIP catalogue record for this book is available from the
British Library.

The publisher gratefully acknowledges permission to use the
following copyright material:

Excerpts from the New Revised Standard Version of the Bible:
Anglicised Edition, © 1989. 1995, Division of Christian Education
of the National Council of the Churches of Christ in the United
States of America. Used by permission. All rights reserved.

Printed and bound by John Dollin Printing Services Ltd,
Whitchurch, Hampshire, RG28 7BB

CONTENTS

*A glossary of the words highlighted in **bold** is at the back of the book*

CHAPTER ONE

Will decides to go on a quest

Will Power wanted to go on a quest. He was dressed, as usual, in his superhero clothes and felt prepared for anything. Will wondered what sort of quest it would be. Would it be a mission to help save people? Or would he find a secret code to break? Perhaps it would be a treasure hunt, with clues to find along the way. If so, he thought there might be treasure at the end.

Will was keen to take his dog, Willy Nilly, with him on his quest. He thought Willy Nilly would be a good companion even if he did get into mischief. It still amused Will to think about the name he had chosen for his dog. Willy Nilly had been into everything when he was a puppy, without a care in the world. He could not make choices in the way Will could. As a dog he had **instinct** only and just went on ahead and did things without thinking. The name Willy Nilly had seemed just right for him.

Will, on the other hand, knew he had **free will** and that he was able to make choices. He had been learning how to use his **reason** to help him make up his mind about what choices to make. He was realising that sensible, wise choices usually had better consequences. Making them needed **willpower**, though, which was essential. Will remembered the time when he had been given a box of chocolates on his last birthday. The chocolates were very tempting but he had only had two to begin with. He then put them on one side to enjoy again later. In the meantime, Willy Nilly had found the box and eaten them all. The poor dog had been sick afterwards, but Will simply couldn't feel cross with him.

Will discovered ten clues on his way. You can find out what these were, with Will, as you follow his journey through the book. But what was prompting Will to go on the quest in the first place, I wonder? And did he find the clues in a logical order? Even more important, what had Will discovered by the time he reached the end? Continue reading to find out.

CHAPTER TWO

Will begins his quest

Will was busy thinking about his quest. He thought he might ask his mum for some ideas. She had told him about her past adventures and might have a few suggestions to make. When Will asked Mum, however, she was feeling cross with him because he had just come in with his clothes all wet again. It had been raining three mornings in a row now and, each time he had gone out, his mum had told him to put his coat on. Will knew he should have done as she'd asked, but he now had to suffer the consequences of ignoring her – he was wet and that had annoyed his mum.

Instead of giving him ideas, Will's mum said firmly, "I'm tired of having to keep finding dry clothes for you. Stop being disobedient! You've done it more than once and that way you are developing a bad habit. You must RESPECT YOUR FATHER AND MOTHER."

Will thought this was rather unhelpful and not a good starting point at all. He didn't really know what she meant anyway, although he could tell by the tone of her voice that she was upset with him.

Once he had put on some dry clothes and given Willy Nilly a rubdown to dry off his fur, Will decided to go out and start the quest on his own. He thought he had better put his coat on this time, though. Will was puzzled about the words his mum had used. What did "disobedience" mean? And "**respect**" was a strange word. Will usually called his parents mum and dad, too, and not mother and father. He walked aimlessly down the street, thinking. In the back of his mind he remembered that his mum had told him not to go past the end of the road without asking her first, but he was distracted: Will wanted to understand what his mum meant, but he also wanted to start his adventure.

Willy Nilly dashed on ahead, and Will found it difficult to keep up with him. In his excitement to be out again, Willy Nilly was running all over the place, and the long lead he was on became tangled round a tree. As Will bent down to unravel it, he accidentally let go. When it was untangled, Willy Nilly shot off with the lead trailing behind him. He ran along Mindful Road in the direction of Conscience Common. Before Will knew it, Willy Nilly was darting along a path leading to the field: other dogs were there, and someone was throwing a ball around for them to catch. Willy Nilly was desperate to join in. Just as Will caught up with him, the ball was thrown into the lake and all the dogs, including Willy Nilly, dashed towards it.

Will's heart sank: he knew Willy Nilly would get wet and muddy in the lake. Mum would be mad if he brought him home like this again. He tried to catch Willy Nilly before he jumped in, but Willy Nilly was too quick. He was in the water before Will could reach him. Will couldn't stop in time at the edge. He tripped over the uneven paving slabs and fell straight in. As he was falling, it flashed through Will's mind that his mum would be even madder if he was wet again, too.

Will landed in the water and sank quickly. The water was deep. It covered his head, and he could barely see anything through the murky green. Will tried to kick back up to the surface again, like he did when he was at the swimming pool after jumping in, but he felt his feet trapped by something. The trailing dog lead had become caught round Will's legs. He couldn't breathe and he started to panic, arms flailing and thrashing about. Suddenly a strong pair of hands grabbed him and yanked him to the surface. Will found himself being dragged onto the bank of the lake. He coughed up mouthfuls of dirty water and gulped in air. He had been saved.

The firm hands belonged to a dad who had been feeding the ducks whilst his toddler watched from a pushchair. He asked Will what he had been doing on his own like that. As Will lay there trying to remember what had happened, it suddenly struck him what **obedience** must mean. He had been told to ask his mum if he wanted to go further than the end of the road. He had remembered this when he set off with Willy Nilly but decided to carry on anyway. Will had not done what he was told and that meant he had been disobedient.

Will was helped home by the dad who had saved him. Willy Nilly had also been rescued in the meantime, and they were both wet and bedraggled. Will was very upset. Mum had been worried about where he was and was relieved to see him but angry with him too. When he stopped feeling sorry for himself, Will wondered if his quest had already begun. He had had an adventure but not the one he expected, he thought.

Respecting his father and his mother must mean loving his mum and dad. One of the ways he could do that was by being obedient. There were other ways as well such as listening properly, not answering back, being kind, and being helpful. Can you think of any more?

Why don't you write them down in the box, below?

> I can respect my mum and dad by:

Will remembered how kind Mum was to her own mum, his gran. She visited her, helped her if she needed it, and generally kept an eye on her. He wanted to be like that when he grew up and always take care of his mum and dad.

CHAPTER THREE

Will gets into more trouble

Will was keen to continue his quest. He thought he would ask his dad this time. Surprisingly, Dad replied by telling Will about the Ten Commandments. Will hadn't heard about them before.

"Long ago, Moses, the leader of the Israelite people, was on a quest to guide his people to the Promised Land. The people had begun to make some very bad choices and as a result the quest was not going well," he said. "God gave Moses the Ten Commandments to guide them in choosing the right thing to do. They are still very useful today and apply to us, too."

Dad had heard all about Will's adventure on the Common and knew Mum had already mentioned the Commandment about respecting your father and mother. "Another one is YOU SHALL NOT KILL," he said. "It includes being so angry with someone that you take **revenge** and also includes being aggressive and bullying."

Will certainly didn't think that he was likely to kill anyone. He was unaware of ever being very angry and wasn't at all sure what taking revenge meant. He was just about to ask some more questions when his older sister, Jo, came buzzing in with one of his toys. It was Will's favourite Lego rocket which his best friend, Samir, had given him for his birthday. Jo had decided to play with it but hadn't thought to ask him first.

"Hey, give that to me," he said angrily. "You haven't asked me yet whether you can play with it." Willy Nilly wasn't helping much as he clearly wanted to join in the game his sister was playing. Will was even more annoyed when Jo said that she knew someone who had a better Lego rocket than his.

Will reached over to try and grab the rocket back, but Jo was too quick and moved out of the way. She held the rocket up in the air out of his reach. It was an awkward shape which she was unused to, and it suddenly slipped out of her hand onto the floor. The rocket landed with such a crash that all the pieces fell apart. Will was really upset. His dad had seen what had happened and asked Jo to apologise. She felt rather ashamed and began to feel sorry. By now, however, Will was so angry that he wanted to break something of Jo's to pay her back.

Will rushed outside and saw his sister's bike by the garage. He knew how much she liked it. Will thought he would feel better if he picked up the hammer that was lying on the floor of the garage and hit the bike with it. Just once would be enough. Willy Nilly barked furiously at Will, as though to warn him, but he still went ahead and did it. Instead of feeling better, to his surprise, Will felt worse. He felt ashamed and wished he hadn't damaged Jo's bike.

Later on that afternoon Jo set off to cycle to karate. One part of the route was down a steep hill. When she tried to brake, however, it didn't work. Will had pushed the brake cable out of line when he smashed the bike. Jo hurtled down the hill, unable to stop, and swerved to avoid a car parked at the bottom. But she was going too fast and lost her balance. The bike crashed over onto the road and she fell off, hurting herself very badly. A passer-by rang for an ambulance which took her to hospital.

Mum was called. When she arrived at the hospital, she was horrified to find that Jo had a deep cut on her knee which had to be stitched. No bones were broken, but there was a lot of blood and she was badly shaken up.

It didn't take Will long to realise the consequences of his action. The bike had been more badly damaged than he had intended and, as a result, Jo could have been killed. Fortunately Jo was safe, but Will still felt very shocked by what he had done. It would have been terrible if she had been killed. And he had been so convinced that he wouldn't ever kill anyone.

Dad, too, was very upset about the accident, but was wise enough to explain to Will that his fault had been in angrily taking revenge. Will hadn't deliberately tried to hurt his sister. This had been an accident, and there was a difference. Can you see the difference as well?

Instead of "putting right a wrong" like superheroes are supposed to on a quest, Will had seen a wrong and made it worse. He thought rather sadly that he was going backwards rather than forwards. Will didn't feel very proud of himself. He had behaved badly, without thinking about the consequences. Will thought he would make it up to his sister by helping her in some way. He knew she was being bullied at school because she was the only girl in her class who couldn't swim. Even though Jo was three years older than Will, she was still frightened of the water. Two children were calling her horrid names, and he could see how hurt she was. Will decided to go to the swimming pool with Jo as often as he could and help her learn to swim. Besides, ever since falling in the pond, he knew how important it was to be able to swim properly.

Jo was glad of Will's encouragement, and it helped her to overcome her fear. She began to enjoy splashing around in the water and soon found the confidence to swim. Will was proud of her. The class bullies had no reason to pick on her anymore. "Bullying is so unkind," Will thought. "If the bullies had spent less time upsetting Jo and more on enjoying swimming themselves, how much happier we would've all been".

After that, Will kept an eye on Jo and resolved that, if there were any more signs of bullying in the future, he would encourage her to tell her a grown up about it without delay.

Write in the box how you would feel if you were bullied and what you would do.

If I'm bullied, I feel:

If someone bullied me, I would:

I will try not to bully anyone else because:

Will was also struck by how much more determined Jo became, the more she was encouraged. He believed it gave another meaning to the expression, "Where there's a will, there's a way!" Can you see both meanings? If so, why don't you write them both down in the box, below?

One meaning is:

The other meaning is:

CHAPTER FOUR

Will learns about keeping promises

Will was playing on the computer. He moved tiles round in the game to double up numbers but got stuck: he couldn't move any more of them because the board was full. Will thought about the Commandments he had been discovering on his quest. He didn't know yet either how to finish the computer game, or where to find more Commandments. "I wonder what the next one will be," he thought. "Who shall I ask?"

Will's grandad was collecting him from school the next day. Will wondered if he knew about the Commandments. Grandad had been in the air force before he retired and had many stories about the daring missions he had been on. He explained to Will that the Commandments are not like the orders he had received in those days. Instead, they are helpful rules God has given us for making the right choices.

Grandad said that another Commandment is YOU SHALL NOT COMMIT ADULTERY. He said this Commandment was for grown up people who loved each other and made marriage promises on their wedding day. These mean they should be faithful to each other when they are married and not go off with someone else. Grandad said he loved Will's gran very much. He explained that love is not just a romantic feeling, although some romance gave a sparkle now and then, like when he gave her some flowers. Love is a word which means looking out for people by being kind, generous, supportive and encouraging. (All the things his parents were to him, Will thought to himself.) Marrying someone means promising to love your partner like this for the rest of your life.

"It isn't always easy," Grandad said. "Sometimes your partner can be irritating or you feel cross with them. When that happens, you have to make up your mind to keep on loving your partner. Try and remember that love is a decision, Will. Deciding not to, can have some serious consequences, you know."

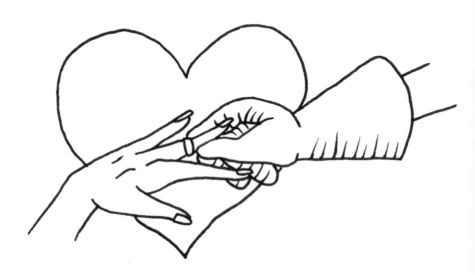

Will could see now that it was a choice that Grandad sometimes had to make, to keep on loving his gran. "For example, if she's being bossy or annoying, I have to stop myself getting irritable or bad tempered with her as that would only make things worse," Grandad said. "She does the same when I'm grumpy and so we don't fall out for long. That way we've always been able to keep our marriage promises. We've stayed together and remained faithful to each other, even though there have been moments when we've been tempted to go off with someone else."

"Of course," Grandad added, "some couples do find it impossible to stay together no matter how hard they try to keep their marriage promises. We wouldn't want to judge people if they do split up."

Grandad decided to explain how important promises are. He said that if someone asked Will to do something and he said yes, then that was a promise. Once the promise was made, it should be kept. A promise should not be made if it was going to be broken. If Will were to make a promise to someone, the other person would rely on it and would be upset if Will broke the promise. For example, if Will promised to help Grandad do some gardening and then decided not to, Grandad would be doubly upset: Grandad would still need the help, and Will would have broken his promise.

Will gathered that promises are always important, from the time you first started making them through to when you were grown up. Yesterday, for example, Mum had asked Will for help in the kitchen. He had said yes, he would do the washing up. She relied on his promise and was grateful for the help.

Grandad pointed out that one of the biggest promises Will would ever make would be to love someone in marriage. In the meantime, the more he practised using willpower to keep a promise, the easier it would become. Will would then be able to keep very important promises like a marriage promise.

Can you remember making any promises? If so, what were they? And can you remember any promises made to you?

Write about some of them in the box.

I made a promise to:

Someone else promised me that they would:

If a promise is made to me, I feel:

If a promise to me is broken, I feel:

CHAPTER FIVE

Will finds out about stealing

Will was feeling pleased about the progress he was making in his quest. Although the route it had taken was unexpected, Will had nevertheless discovered some surprising clues. As a result, he was finding out about what choices to make and the right thing to do.

Will was sitting in class doing his best to focus on what his teacher was saying. It was RE and she was talking about Moses. Will's ears pricked up when his teacher mentioned the Ten Commandments. She started to list the ones he already knew. His mind began to wander. Just at the point she mentioned a new one, YOU SHALL NOT STEAL, he was distracted by a Smiggle pencil that George, one of his friends, had out on the table. It was new and shiny with a lovely sharp point. Will really liked the look of George's pencil and wished he had one, too. It was just what he needed for his drawing homework. Without even thinking, Will took the pencil whilst George was helping to give out some worksheets and hid it in his drawer.

Will immediately felt ashamed of what he had done. This was his friend. How could he treat him like that? What on earth was he dreaming of? He wouldn't like it if George did that to him, would he? Will felt sorry. He could put it right very quickly by putting the pencil back, before George even knew it had been taken, and so that is what he did.

Will thought perhaps this was what was meant by listening to his **conscience**. He couldn't see, touch, or actually hear his conscience, but something inside him had prompted him to feel ashamed, sorry for what he had done, and want to make amends. Will realised how relieved he was that George had not found out, as he would have been very sad to lose his pencil. Will also thought that he would not have been happy if he had kept the pencil. He would have lost his **self-esteem** and felt bad; now he felt good about himself instead.

Will was thinking about what had happened on his way home from school. As he drew near to the house, he could hear Willy Nilly barking. It was not his usual welcoming yelp, but an alarmed sort of whine. Will went to see what had happened. Willy Nilly was standing at the bottom of one of the trees in the garden, looking up into the branches. Will followed the direction he was looking in and saw an animal trapped in the tree. It looked like a small kitten. Will knew there was a fox in the neighbourhood. He thought that perhaps the kitten had been frightened by the fox and shot up the tree to escape. Once the fox had gone, it had been too afraid to climb down again.

Will remembered that superheroes were good at rescuing and decided to help the kitten. He climbed the tree and hauled himself up to the level of the kitten. It was alarmingly high up. He tried not to be afraid. If he didn't look down then he wouldn't feel dizzy. Will could be brave because he was doing something helpful and good. He reached for the kitten, gently picked it up, and carefully carried it down to the ground. Willy Nilly, in the meantime, yapped encouragingly.

The kitten was safe and sound. It began to purr and rubbed itself against Will's legs. Will was delighted. Willy Nilly jumped around, evidently enjoying having a new companion and being the kitten's protector. Will wondered who owned the kitten. It didn't seem to want to go away and tried to follow him inside. Will thought it might be hungry after its ordeal and asked his mum if he could give it some milk.

"Oh, that's a good idea, Will," Mum said, "but I don't want to encourage a stray into the house." It was too late though: the kitten seemed to feel at home, and both Will and Willy Nilly wanted to look after it.

"I think I'll call the kitten Wilhemina," Will said. "It looks like a girl kitten, and I can call her Mina for short."

"Mina doesn't belong to you and, if someone claims her, then she will have to be returned," Mum warned. Dad added that it would be best if they informed the police in the meantime about finding Mina. Happily, the police asked if Will's family could look after her until her owner could be found, and Dad agreed. Will didn't take any notice because he was too wrapped up in what Mina was getting up to. She quickly became one of the household.

As Will walked to school two days later, he saw a notice pinned up in a shop window with a picture of a kitten just like Mina. The notice said that Mrs Williams, the owner of the kitten, had lost her and was trying to find her. Will felt sick, and his heart sank to his boots because it meant that Mina had an owner already. He didn't want to return her though, and so he didn't say anything to his mum about the notice. Will couldn't bear the thought of losing Mina. But he was ashamed about not telling his mum, straightaway.

That evening Mum came in from work and said she had met Mina's owner on the way home. Mrs Williams, who was an elderly lady, had been calling at each house in the road, searching for her lost kitten. She had stopped Will's mum to ask if she knew where it was. Mum then explained everything that had happened and how they had been looking after the kitten until her owner could be found.

"Mina will have to be returned to Mrs Williams," Mum said gently to Will. "It would be stealing otherwise." Will, who knew superheroes always try to be brave especially if they are on a quest, was still, nevertheless, close to tears. He then admitted he had seen the notice and already knew Mina had an owner.

"Oh dear, Will, what a shame!" Mum said. "I'm really sorry, as I know how fond you are of Mina. But, sadly, you made the wrong choice. Looking after her when she needed it was the right choice,  but not returning her when her owner was found, was the wrong one."

Mum said Will should put it right by returning Mina to Mrs Williams. When Will saw how happy she was to have her kitten back, he was glad. Will's rescue mission had been a success after all. Mrs Williams would have been very sad if she had lost her kitten forever, as she lived alone and the kitten was company for her. Mrs Williams decided to keep the name that Will had chosen for her. She liked the name Mina, and it would be a way of thanking Will for rescuing her. Suddenly Will felt much better about himself and his self-esteem rose.

Have you ever had to make a difficult choice?

Write about it in the box.

Even though it was difficult, I chose to:

CHAPTER SIX

Will learns about lying and cheating

Will was feeling just a bit sad and lonely after Mina had been returned to Mrs Williams. Willy Nilly seemed to sense it; he kept Will company and stayed close by, quietly. Will felt much better by the end of the week. He wanted to carry on with the quest: he was sure there was more to discover. The route seemed to be going from one Commandment to another, a bit like signposts showing him the way. He wondered what the next one would be and where it would lead him.

In the meantime, Will decided to work on the project which he had been set. The theme was Natural History, and he and some of his classmates had decided to do their project on dinosaurs of the Jurassic period. The first five children in his class to complete ten pages were to be taken on a special outing with the Year above to the Natural History Museum. Will was keen to go as soon as possible because a new exhibit had been installed recently, and he was desperate to see it. It was a huge dinosaur skeleton that had only just been discovered and which didn't even have a name yet.

The class teacher, who had just finished talking about making wise decisions and sensible choices, teased the children by calling the new dinosaur a Temptasaurus. "I have heard some fascinating details about it," she joked. "It used its long, sharp teeth for crunching up reason and its ferocious claws for tearing willpower apart!" Will had laughed but, nevertheless, it sounded both terrifying and thrilling at the same time.

As Will reached for his books to do some more research, his dad came in from doing **jury** service at **court**. Dad, and the other jurors, had to listen to what witnesses had to say about a crime and then decide if the accused person was **innocent** or **guilty**. Dad remarked that reaching a decision would not be easy as one of the witnesses had lied. He said that this broke the Commandment that says, YOU SHALL NOT GIVE FALSE WITNESS AGAINST YOUR NEIGHBOUR.

Will only half heard Dad mention another Commandment as his mind was on his project. He didn't concentrate on what his dad was saying. Will was a bit confused by the word "neighbour", anyway, because his family had kindly neighbours next door. He thought it was strange that one of the Commandments should only apply to them.

Six children in the class, including Will, had completed ten pages by Monday morning. Will wondered how their teacher would pick five. As he handed in his book, Laurie, one of the other five, reported that Will had been cheating by copying Laurie's work. This was a lie. Will had borrowed a library book to use for the project and had shared it with Laurie so that he could use it as well. However, the teacher believed Laurie and told Will that, as there were only five places, he would not be able to go.

Will felt very disappointed. He had worked so hard to be one of the first to complete ten pages. He felt badly let down by Laurie who, instead of repaying his kindness to him, had accused him of copying and cheating. Will also thought the teacher's decision was unfair because it was based on a lie about him. Will spoke up for himself but it was too late, the damage had been done. As there were only five places, their teacher would not change her mind.

Dad later explained to Will what giving false witness meant. "It doesn't just apply in court when a witness lies about what they saw. It can happen at any time such as when Laurie told a lie about you," he said. "And the word 'neighbour' means anyone who is in need and not just someone who lives next door."

Will was angry and wanted to take revenge on Laurie. But then he remembered what had happened to his sister Jo when he damaged her bike and how disastrous that had been. Will thought he would ask Dad what to do.

"Why don't you keep working really hard on the project," Dad suggested. "It's an interesting subject and I think you are enjoying learning about it. It will also earn you some merit with your teacher. She will be pleased that you want to persevere, even though you can't go to the museum on the visit." Sympathising, he then said, "I know how upset you're feeling and disappointed about not being able to go yet, so I'll take you instead at the weekend." Will thought this was a brilliant idea. He felt encouraged and decided to continue working on his project until it was finished.

On the school trip, the class teacher happened to overhear Laurie boasting to the other four children in his class about what he done. Laurie thought he had got away with it. Now however, the teacher would decide on a consequence for Laurie when they returned to school. In the meantime the teacher had submitted all the best projects, including Will's, to the school competition for the best project of the year. When the time came for judging, the head teacher thought Will's was so good that it was selected, and Will won a prize.

CHAPTER SEVEN

Will is tempted again

By now Will expected that the next signpost in his quest would be another Commandment. It was a bit like a treasure hunt with a series of clues. He was beginning to wonder if, once he had found all the clues, he might find treasure at the end.

Will had been noticing in the playground at school recently, that there was a child who was taking the friends of other children away and forming a new gang of his own. The children remaining were feeling left out because they had lost their friends. Will felt sorry for them and thought it was unfair. He wondered what to do and decided to talk to his dad about it when he got home.

Dad believed this was a good moment to mention the Commandment which says, YOU SHALL NOT COVET OTHER PEOPLE.[1] He explained that to covet someone meant to wish for a person so much that you wanted to take them away or steal them, which the child in class was doing. So as to explain a bit more, he mentioned some familiar stories where bad characters wanted good characters so much that they trapped and stole them. One story, for example, was Hansel and Gretel.

Can you think of any more stories with bad characters who coveted good characters? There should be some, which you can list in the box below.

This is my list of stories:

[1] The Anglican Church has one Commandment "you shall not covet", while the Roman Catholic Church specifies two different ways we might covet in two separate Commandments.

Will immediately dismissed any idea that he might covet people. He couldn't see how the Commandment related to his quest much, either. He soon forgot about it anyway because he was practising hard for the school concert. Will liked performing, but learning the music was difficult. He really had to make himself practise, when he would rather have been watching television or playing a computer game. Will's piece was a recorder duet, but the other player, Tim, was better than he was. This didn't make it any easier.

Tim said he would help Will learn the piece. They took it in turn to go to each other's home every day to practise. At the concert they both played perfectly and were congratulated by everyone. Will was grateful to Tim, who was also good at other things like football and running. He began to wish Tim was his best friend. They each had a best friend already though: Will's best friend was Samir and Tim's was Pete. Pete had been in hospital for a while now after an operation on his leg and so Tim didn't see him very often. Without thinking, Will asked Tim if he could be his best friend. Tim was lonely, but he wanted to remain loyal to Pete who needed friends even more while he was in hospital.

Tim had a brainwave. He wanted to be friends with Will and suggested that he should come with him to visit Pete in hospital. Will could bring Samir with him, as well. That way they could all be friends. Tim would no longer be on his own so much and Pete would have more visitors in hospital. Will's mum thought this was a very good idea. She said superheroes did kind things like visit sick people in hospital. Mum said she would bake some brownies for Will to take in for Pete, in case the hospital food wasn't very appetising. She also said that he could borrow her iPad so that Pete could play Cooking Fever and at least pretend he was eating something delicious.

Will was glad about Tim's solution. He felt relieved because, somewhere in the back of his mind, his conscience had been nagging him about not coveting someone else's friend. If Tim had agreed to Will's suggestion to being his best friend, the consequences would have been sad. Tim's way meant everyone was happy. They could form their own gang now, Will thought. What name would you choose for Will's gang?

Tim's solution meant everyone was included, and no-one was left out, feeling lonely. Do you ever notice children who are left out? How do you think they feel? Do you try and include them, like Tim?

CHAPTER EIGHT

Will learns about jealousy

Will's teacher had heard about what had been happening in the playground. She thought it was time for a discussion about jealousy. So, in the next RE lesson, she mentioned that the Commandments explain, YOU SHALL NOT COVET OTHER PEOPLES' BELONGINGS.[1]

Will tried to listen to what his teacher was saying about not coveting things, or being **jealous** of what people had. It wasn't easy and needed willpower. Will sat up when he heard that because he knew all about willpower now.

"So," he thought to himself, "if I like my friend's toy very much and want it, I can use my willpower to decide not to be jealous." But it didn't sound easy.

---

[1] As referred to in the last chapter, the Roman Catholic Church makes a distinction between coveting people and things.

Will's teacher was reassuring. "If you decide not to be jealous just once, it will be easier next time and then become a habit," she said.

Will's teacher also explained that boasting about your belongings could lead to other children being jealous of you, so this was something to avoid too. Will was a bit confused and hurt by what she said. He liked to say how lovely his things were or what a wonderful dog Willy Nilly was, for example. It hadn't occurred to him that it might make people jealous.

Will suddenly remembered that he hadn't seen much of Willy Nilly recently because of the hospital visiting and the fun he had been having with the gang. He wondered if Willy Nilly was missing him and decided to spend some more time with him.

"Can I take Willy Nilly out for an extra long walk on Conscience Common?" he asked his mum. "He likes running wild there." Mum agreed to take him at the weekend. "The whole family can go, and we can take a picnic with us as well," she said.

The following Saturday they set off on the outing. Will followed Willy Nilly as he chased across the Common and through the trees. He had brought a ball with him which he was throwing as far as he could for Willy Nilly to run and catch. Willy Nilly was having a wonderful time. Will's sister Jo, in the meantime, was helping to lay out the picnic. There were all sorts of delicious things to eat, and she was looking forward to it.

Without any warning, the ball landed close by, and Jo was cross when she saw Willy Nilly charging over. She was jealous, too. She wished she had a dog of her own to play with, like Willy Nilly, who loved her as much as he seemed to love Will. The ball rolled right into the middle of the picnic. Willy Nilly dived in to  catch it, just as Jo was turning round to reach for the crisps. She overbalanced and tripped over. She landed right on the knee which had had stitches after her cycling accident and grazed it again. When he saw what had happened, Willy Nilly was fixed to the spot. But Jo was so upset that, after picking herself up, she kicked him without even thinking. Willy Nilly was startled and snarled fiercely at her. Jo leapt back in alarm and tumbled over again. As she fell, she yelled in a jealous rage, "Willy Nilly is dangerous and should be put down."

Mum tried to calm Jo. She inspected the grazed knee. It stopped hurting very quickly and wasn't nearly as bad as all that. No real harm had been done, and she had over-reacted. Willy Nilly, on the other hand, had been deliberately kicked, and Will was beside himself. Willy Nilly had been playing quite happily and had only got in the way accidentally. Will was horrified by his sister's demand: Willy Nilly was certainly not dangerous, and the thought of him being put down was too awful for words.

"What you did was wrong," Mum gently explained to Jo. "Although Willy Nilly is Will's dog, he's part of the family. Will knows you're fond of Willy Nilly and is pleased if you play with him, especially if he's doing something else. It means Willy Nilly has another companion." Jo began to realise how upsetting her behaviour had been, particularly for Will. It was spoiling the picnic. After struggling with her conscience, she decided to say sorry to Will.

Will, however, wondered why he should forgive Jo for being so horrid. He felt grumpy and ready to pick a fight. Mum patiently explained that Will should now forgive his sister. If he didn't, they could not make up. She said it was a choice he had to make, with consequences. Either he could choose not to forgive his sister and remain hurt and moody, or he could decide to forgive her and be friends again; and they could then all begin to enjoy their picnic once more.

What would you have chosen to do? Think for a minute and then write your answer in the box below.

I would have chosen to:

CHAPTER NINE

Will finds a guide

Will had now discovered various Commandments on his quest. They were pointing him in the direction to take. If he ignored them, he ended up on the wrong path. Will knew that there were ten altogether, and his quest would not be over until he had found the others.

Not long after, Will's gran became very ill, so ill that everyone thought she was going to die. While Will was visiting her, the priest from her church came to give her a special blessing. Father Wright was very comforting. He said that if she died, Will's gran would go to heaven to join God our Father, and be happy forever. She had led a good life doing her best to love God and everyone else around her. Heaven was a reward Gran would receive at the end of her life and was what God had promised.

Will's ears pricked up when Father Wright mentioned a reward. He thought he would ask Father Wright about it. Father Wright seemed ready to listen. Will told him about the quest and how, so far, it had seemed to be testing him on the best choices to make in life. It hadn't been easy but Will had discovered some Commandments along the way which had been clues to help him. Will explained he wanted to find the others but wasn't sure where. He was wondering where they would all lead and what he would find at the end of his quest.

Father Wright was interested in Will's story and very encouraging. He began by saying that God had commanded us as follows: "You shall love the Lord your God with all your heart, and with all your soul, and with all your strength, and with all your mind; and your neighbour as yourself." Father Wright explained that this statement summed up all the Ten Commandments.

Clearly, Will had been finding out about loving his neighbour on his quest so far. The Commandments he had found had been showing him how to do it. "But there is more to it than that, Will," Father Wright said. "Loving God is really important, and there are some more Commandments to help us. Before you continue on your quest and find out what these are, I want to explain how close God is to us. God is not on another planet. God is with us here on earth as well as in heaven. We show we are with God in return when we choose to love God. Loving our neighbour is one way of doing this. It's a bit like being in a team where, by working together, we show support for our team leader.

Will was puzzled. He knew he could make wrong choices sometimes which meant he disobeyed some of the Commandments. It was hard at times. "If God really loves us and wants us to love him in return, why can we make wrong choices?" he asked.

"Well, the answer to that, Will, is that God loves us so much that God wants us to be free to make up our own minds to do what is right." Father Wright said, "If we weren't free and didn't have free will, we would be like puppets on strings. Marionettes are not nearly as lovable as real people."

Will remembered the story of Pinocchio, a naughty puppet, and how much he had wanted to be a real boy. It was not until he had learnt several difficult lessons about how to behave and be kind to people that he became human. Pinocchio had then turned into a very endearing child indeed and was much more lovable. "You were made in God's likeness, you know, and you are one of God's children already and not a puppet," Father Wright said.

Father Wright thought that was probably enough talk for a while. It was time for him to visit some other patients, anyway.

"Why don't you have a think about God's love and being part of God's team, Will?" he said.

Gran was fast asleep, and so Will had a few moments to start thinking. He began to wonder if his quest was all about finding God's love for him and learning how to love him in return. Were his wise choices, and the wise choices of the people he had met so far on his quest, ways of him finding God's love, and of God loving him in return? Will just hadn't thought about it this way before and it was an important discovery.

Can you remember any of the wise choices made during Will's quest?

There are quite a few, so instead of writing the wise choices down, you could say them out loud.

CHAPTER TEN

Will turns a corner

Will went to see Gran in hospital again the following weekend. She was still quite poorly. Will hoped Father Wright would be there to tell him about the next Commandment. The quest wasn't over yet and he wanted to reach the end.

Father Wright wanted to help Will and called by on his hospital round a few minutes later. He told Will the very first Commandment was YOU SHALL WORSHIP THE LORD YOUR GOD AND NOT WORSHIP FALSE GODS.[1] Father Wright said there were two parts to this: the first was about worshipping God and the second was about not worshipping false gods. "We worship God by believing, trusting and loving God as best we can, and by thanking God in our prayers," he said. "Going to church is one important way we can do this."

---

[1] The Anglican Church splits this Commandment into two separate Commandments.

Father Wright went on to explain that the second part means that God should not be replaced by anyone or anything else. God gave Moses the Ten Commandments in the first place because the Israelites were tempted to worship a golden calf instead of God. Father Wright said there were many other types of false gods, another name for which is **idol**. Sometimes people start to idolise things which become too important to them like money, celebrities, mobile phones and computer games. They begin to think about them too much and don't have enough time for God: they substitute them for God.

Can you think of any more? Write them in the box below.

Father Wright said that if Will thought hard, he would probably be able to remember when his gran followed this Commandment. Just then Father Wright was called away on an emergency. Will decided to sit by her bedside for a while and think about some of the times he had spent with her. Gran certainly was kind and caring. Will remembered the things they had done together such as the outings they had been on and the holidays they had shared. Gran had always encouraged him in what he was doing, sympathised if he had been disappointed over something, or looked after him if he had hurt himself. Will remembered the sleepovers, the cakes she used to make, and going out to pick blackberries or collect conkers with her. She had been firm though, and had often said she wouldn't stand any nonsense. Will knew too that Gran had always wanted to go to church on Sunday and remembered to say her prayers. And she had encouraged Will to do the same when he stayed overnight with her.

On one occasion, Gran and Will had been to see Jack and the Beanstalk at the theatre. Jack had got a lot of gold in the story and after the show Will had started to talk about what fun it would be to win the Lottery. Gran had said that money wasn't everything, and it didn't necessarily make you happy. She had even said that money could be an idol. A minute later, Will had tripped over something on the pavement: it was a purse with fifty pounds in it. He had started to imagine what he might spend the money on; he could buy another Lego set for instance.

Gran had interrupted his train of thought saying, "We must find the owner and return the purse, Will. You shouldn't love money so much. Besides, if you keep the money without trying to find the owner first, it would be stealing." Gran had looked inside the purse and found the name and address of the person it belonged to. "It's not far from where you live, Will," she said. "Let's hand it back in person straightaway rather than take it to a police station. It'll be on our way home."

The owner was very pleased and relieved when Gran handed her the purse. Her family had just moved house, and there was very little money to spare. She could not have afforded to lose it. When she saw Will she said, "I have a son about your age. I wonder if you are at the same school he will be starting at. His name is Samir." She had then introduced him to Will. That was how Samir and Will had first met and they had, of course, become firm friends – and all because of what Will's gran had decided to do with the purse.

Can you see how Gran followed the Commandment and showed her love of God? Describe how in the box below.

Gran showed her love for God by:

CHAPTER ELEVEN

Will nears the end

W ill had been sitting with his gran for quite a while now. Just as he was beginning to wonder if it was time to go home and when his mum was going to collect him, Grandad turned up to see Gran as well. Since the time Grandad had told him about one of the Commandments a while ago, Will had of course found quite a few more and wanted to tell him. Also, Grandad might be able to continue where Father Wright had left off and tell him about another Commandment on the list.

"Yes, all right, Will," Grandad said, as Gran dozed. "Another Commandment says, YOU SHALL NOT TAKE THE NAME OF THE LORD YOUR GOD IN VAIN." Grandad began to explain. "We are all God's children and God knows each one of us individually by name. We are so important to God that our names are written on the palm of God's hand," he said. "The clue, Will, is in how we use a name and how in particular we use God's holy name in return. One important way is to remember God each day by praying and asking God to help us to do everything in God's holy name."

Grandad then explained that even though we may say God's name respectfully in our prayers, using it disrespectfully does happen. Sometimes if we are upset or angry, we exclaim angrily using God's name: this is disrespectful and is taking God's name in vain. If we use God's name very offensively, it's called blasphemy.

Sometimes people make promises called oaths and swear on God's name to keep them. These promises should only be made if they can be kept. "Do you remember me telling you about the importance of keeping a promise?" Grandad asked. Will did, and also remembered that the witness in Dad's court case had promised to tell the truth. He asked Grandad about it.

"The witness in Dad's court case placed his hand on the Bible which contains God's name and then swore to tell the truth. But he broke his oath and lied. Not only did the witness break the law but, even more importantly, he also broke this Commandment as well," Grandad said.

Just then Gran woke up. She started whispering something. It sounded like a prayer and she seemed to be saying, "Our Father who art in heaven, hallowed by thy name". Will knew the prayer and wondered if he should join in with her. Gran smiled at him, and he grinned. She must have been feeling a bit better because she teased him by asking him to find the bag of butterscotch at the back of her bedside cupboard. She knew full well that he wouldn't be able to reach it without knocking over all the other stuff in front. Gran laughed when everything crashed onto the floor. Will was annoyed and angrily used God's name.

"No Will," Gran said, "don't use words like that, it's disrespectful. Laugh at yourself instead. Let's show we want to be on God's team and finish our prayers."

Will wondered if she had a point, as he was about to pop a sweet into his mouth. It was better feeling pleased that Gran was recovering, than cross about knocking things over. And Will knew he could have the sweet in a minute, after their prayers.

How did Will's gran show respect for God's name?

Write your answer in the box.

Gran showed respect for God's name by:

CHAPTER TWELVE

Will goes the distance

Will had almost reached the end of his quest. There was only one more Commandment to find. He was getting really rather tired and restless at the hospital by now and his mum still hadn't come to collect him. Will was hungry as well and wished he could be at home, playing with Willy Nilly. Just then a nurse popped her head round the door to leave a message that his mum was delayed but would be there to collect him as soon as she could. When Grandad saw how dismayed Will looked, he decided to take him to the hospital cafe for some orange juice and a biscuit.

On the way Grandad pointed out that for a quest to be worthwhile, superheroes must endure trials and need to be patient to overcome them so as to reach the end successfully. Will remembered some of the computer games he played and how the higher the level he reached in them, the harder they became.

"You have been very patient Will and persevered so well," he said. "On the way back to Gran's ward, I'll tell you about another Commandment before you go home. It is REMEMBER TO KEEP HOLY THE LORD'S DAY." He began to explain what this meant. "The Bible describes how God created the world in six days and then rested on the seventh day. One of the meanings in this story is that God wants us to rest on one day each week and for it to be a holy day. Jewish people keep their holy day, called the Sabbath, on Saturday, but for Christians the holy day is Sunday. That is because it is the day Jesus rose from the dead. It is called the Lord's Day. We keep it holy by resting from work and going to church to worship God."

Grandad explained that shops are sometimes closed on Sundays, or not open for as long as they usually are during the week. Will remembered receiving some money on his last birthday and not being able to spend it at his favourite toy shop on a Sunday because it was closed. "And most office workers have Sunday off too," Grandad added. Will had noticed Dad only worked on weekdays and now understood the reason why.

When they reached Gran's bedside, she was awake but agitated. Will was concerned and asked her what the matter was. Gran said it was Sunday today and she wanted to go to church like she usually did. It was Will's turn to laugh now because it was Saturday, not Sunday.

"Oh, silly me!" Gran said, "I've been so poorly and taking so much medicine that I am confused about which day of the week it is. I want to make sure that I go to church on the right day, and I really thought it was Sunday." Even though she was upset about her forgetfulness, Gran didn't use any swear words, Will noticed. She was amused at herself, instead.

"Do you remember when the whole family went on holiday to Dorset, Will?" she asked. "The second day was a Sunday, and I searched online to find the nearest church so that we could all go to pray together in the morning." Will recalled that he had been disappointed that they couldn't go straight to the beach. Gran had said first things first and the day would not be complete otherwise.

After church they had gone for a walk along the beach, which Gran called the Jurassic coastline, where they found a perfect ammonite fossil in a recent rock downfall. Gran said they were still occasionally discovering full dinosaur skeletons there, even today. It was when Will had first become interested in dinosaurs. They had played on the beach, swum in the sea and gone rock-pooling.

"What a lovely holiday it was, Will," Gran murmured sleepily. Then she added something about finding treasure round every corner in this life if we only knew where to look for it. And it didn't have anything to do with gold or riches either, she added, before falling asleep again. As she did so, Will realised how Gran had kept this Commandment. I expect you have, too. He also realised that he had discovered all the Commandments now.

Can you remember all the Commandments that Will has found? See if you can list them all out loud.

CHAPTER THIRTEEN

Will reaches the end of his quest

ather Wright popped back to say goodbye to Gran before he left the hospital. If Will was still there, he wanted to finish telling him about the Ten Commandments. Will hadn't left yet and was puzzling about the last thing Gran had said about treasure. He was puzzled about the list too. He had discovered the last few Commandments, but they seemed to be the first ones and not the last.

Father Wright explained that the Ten Commandments can be divided into two groups: the first are about loving God, and the others are about loving other people, referred to as our "neighbour". "As I mentioned in our first conversation, Will, when we do one we do the other," he said. "The more we love our neighbour, the closer we come to God, our Father, as well. God wants us to love our neighbour and, in that way, show we love God." Father Wright thought that Will had discovered the Commandments about loving his neighbour first because he would then know how to love God better. Finding the Commandments in an unusual order had been a helpful approach for Will in his quest.

Father Wright went on to say that God loves us very much and wants us to be happy. God will always be by our side: we can rely on God to help us. God has given us the Commandments because we sometimes make mistakes and wrong choices which make us unhappy. By following God's Commandments we can make wise choices and be happy instead.

Will asked Father Wright what the treasure was that Gran had mentioned. Father Wright thought for a minute and said she probably meant all those times when we make a wise choice and the consequences turn out to be really good. "Oh," it dawned on Will, "like meeting a new friend because Gran decided to return the purse, or deciding to forgive my sister and then having an awesome picnic."

Will looked back over his adventures. He had been sad when he disobeyed the Commandments, and it had led to other people being unhappy. Father Wright then explained that if Will was ever tempted to disobey a Commandment, God had given him his conscience. This was another sign of God's love. The voice of his conscience was God's way of prompting Will to make the right choice, and he should listen to it carefully. By means of his conscience, God was showing Will what to do when he was trying to make up his mind and decide. Will remembered the time he had stolen the Smiggle pencil and decided to return it. He also remembered when Jo was being bullied and helping her learn to swim.

Will had enjoyed the quest and learnt so much on the way. He could see now how much God must love him. "God must like adventures," he thought. Father Wright pointed out that the quest had been like a treasure hunt, and God had provided the clues in the form of Commandments for him to find. God's love for Will, knowing how to love God in return, and then being able to live happily with God in heaven, must be the wonderful treasure God wanted Will to find at the end of the quest.

Will thought of all the stories where, after lots of adventures, everyone lived happily ever after. Now, he knew his life would be a quest with lots of adventures and with a happy ending. Will knew there would be difficult choices to make and temptations along the way, but he had found the Commandments to help him. "Where there's a will, there's a way to finding God our Father in this life, and then living with God happily ever after in heaven," Will thought.

Glossary

Instinct - not having to think first before doing something, like animals, for example, which behave automatically

Free will - having a choice about doing something

Reason - what you use to work things out in your mind

Willpower - ability to control your response

Respect - behaving well towards someone

Obedience - doing what you are told to do, for example, by your parents

Revenge - paying someone back if they wrong you

Conscience - inner sense of what is right and wrong given to us by God

Self-esteem - how you think and feel about yourself

Jury - a group of twelve people who decide on the evidence in court if an accused person is innocent or guilty of a crime

Court - where an accused person is tried to find out if he is innocent or guilty of a crime

Innocent - not having done anything wrong

Guilty - responsible for doing something wrong

Jealous - wanting what someone else has

Idol - something or person worshipped or adored

The Ten Commandments

Catholic Church

1. I am the Lord your God: you shall not have strange Gods before me.
2. You shall not take the name of the Lord your God in vain.
3. Remember to keep holy the Lord's Day.
4. Honour your father and mother.
5. You shall not kill.
6. You shall not commit adultery.
7. You shall not steal.
8. You shall not bear false witness against your neighbour.
9. You shall not covet your neighbour's wife.
10. You shall not covet your neighbour's goods.

(Catechism of the Catholic Church)

Anglican Church

1. I am the Lord your God: you shall have no other gods before me.
2. You shall not make for yourself an idol.
3. You shall not make wrongful use of the name of the Lord Your God.
4. Remember the Sabbath day and keep it holy.
5. Honour your father and your mother.
6. You shall not murder.
7. You shall not commit adultery.
8. You shall not steal.
9. You shall not bear false witness against your neighbour.
10. You shall not covet anything that belongs to your neighbour.

Published by Ice House Books

Copyright © 2019 Ice House Books

Written by Zulekha Afzal & Raphaella Thompson
Edited by Samantha Rigby
Designed by Joe Brown
Photography credits overleaf

Ice House Books is an imprint of Half Moon Bay Limited
The Ice House, 124 Walcot Street, Bath, BA1 5BG
www.icehousebooks.co.uk

ISBN 978-1-912867-07-3

Printed in China

Spell-icious Cookery

ICE HOUSE BOOKS

PHOTOGRAPHY

CONTENTS

ROTTEN APPLES
(Toffee Apples)

INGREDIENTS

- 4 Braeburn apples
- lolly sticks/skewers
- 200 g (7 oz) sugar
- 2 tbsp golden syrup
- 20 g (0.7 oz) salted butter
- 75 ml (2.6 fl oz) water
- 1 tsp cider vinegar

Makes: 4 toffee apples
Prep Time: 5 minutes
Cook Time: 10 minutes

METHOD

1 Ensure the apples are washed and push a stick or skewer through each apple (making sure it doesn't come out the other end).

2 In a medium pan over a medium heat, dissolve the sugar, syrup and butter with the water and stir through the vinegar.

3 Turn up the heat gradually and stir until the mixture has a thick, sticky consistency.

4 Before the toffee sauce has a chance to cool down, dip the apples into it so they are fully coated. Leave them to dry on a sheet of baking paper and allow to cool before tucking in.

ORANGE GEMSTONES
(Candied Pumpkin)

INGREDIENTS

- 55 g (2 oz) butter
- 390 g (14 oz) fresh pumpkin, cut into small cubes
- 40 g (1.5 oz) white sugar
- 255 ml (9 fl oz) maple syrup
- 1 tbsp minced fresh ginger
- ½ tsp ground cinnamon

Makes: 12 servings
Prep Time: 10 minutes
Cook Time: 25 to 30 minutes
Extra Time: 2 hours to set

METHOD

1 In a large pan over a medium heat, melt the butter until liquid. Cook the pumpkin in the butter for approximately 20 minutes until tender.

2 Dissolve in the sugar and stir in the syrup, ginger and cinnamon.

3 Remove from the heat and allow to cool.

4 Transfer to a covered bowl and chill in the fridge, allowing it to set for at least two hours. Then serve!

PUMPKIN ILLUSIONS
(Wild Rice Stuffed Pumpkin)

INGREDIENTS

- 225 g (8 oz) wild rice blend
- 120 ml (4.2 fl oz) water
- 400 g (14 oz) fresh spinach
- 3 tbsp olive oil
- 225 g (8 oz) button mushrooms
- 110 g (4 oz) celery, sliced
- 1 small onion, chopped
- 1 tbsp garlic, minced
- 2 tsp fresh thyme, chopped
- 175 g (6 oz) frozen sweetcorn
- 150 g (5.5 oz) canned black beans, rinsed and drained
- 60 g (2 oz) toasted cashews, halved
- small cooking pumpkins, to serve
- sage leaves, for garnish

Makes: 6 servings
Prep Time: 20 to 30 minutes
Cook Time: 2 hours to 2 hours, 40 minutes

Turn the page for the method.

METHOD

1 Start by making the wild rice blend according to the directions, and set it aside in a bowl.

2 Pour the water into a pan and bring it to the boil. Add the spinach and cook it until it's wilted. Drain and cool the spinach, then squeeze it dry, roughly chop it and add it to the bowl of rice.

3 Heat a tablespoon of oil in the pan over a medium heat and add the mushrooms, celery, onion, half a tablespoon of garlic and a teaspoon of the thyme. Sauté for 10 minutes or until all the liquid has evaporated, then stir in the sweetcorn and black beans and sauté for a further three minutes. Next, add the mushroom mixture to the rice mixture, then stir in the cashews and season to taste.

4 Preheat the oven to 175ºC/350ºF/Gas Mark 4. Line a baking tray with foil. Cut the top off your cooking pumpkins and scoop out the seeds and pulp.

5 In a bowl, combine two tablespoons of oil with the remaining garlic and thyme. Brush the mixture around the inside of the pumpkins, then fill them with the rice and vegetable mixture.

6 Put the tops back on and bake in the oven for 1½ to 2 hours, or until the pumpkins are tender when pierced with a knife-tip. Uncover and bake them for a further 10–20 minutes, then garnish with the sage leaves and tuck in!

BUBBLING CAULDRON SOUP
(Pumpkin & Carrot Soup)

INGREDIENTS

- 5 tbsp olive oil
- ½ pumpkin, cubed
- 4 carrots, cubed
- 1 onion, diced
- 1 apple, diced
- 30 ml (1 fl oz) water
- 1 tbsp curry powder
- 375 ml (13.1 fl oz) vegetable stock
- salt and pepper, to taste
- 125 g (4.5 oz) sour cream, for garnish
- coriander, for garnish

Makes: 4 bowls
Prep Time: 10 minutes
Cook Time: 20 to 25 minutes

METHOD

1 In a large pan over a medium heat, add the oil and chopped vegetables. Fry for five minutes while stirring.

2 Add the curry powder, apple and water, and fry for two minutes.

3 Add the stock and let the mixture simmer for 10 minutes, stirring occasionally.

4 Pulse the soup with a hand-blender until smooth. Serve with sour cream and coriander to garnish, and season to taste.

ENCHANTED STONES
(Matcha Macarons)

INGREDIENTS

For the shells:

- 1 free-range egg white
- 30 g (1 oz) granulated sugar
- 40 g (1.5 oz) icing sugar
- 30 g (1 oz) almond flour
- 1 tsp matcha powder

For the filling:

- 70 g (2.5 oz) icing sugar
- 50 g (1.75 oz) cream cheese, room temperature
- 1 tsp milk

Makes: 9
Prep Time: 1 hour, 45 minute
Cook Time: 15 minutes

METHOD

1 With an electric hand mixer, beat the egg white on a medium speed until soft peaks form. Add half of the granulated sugar and turn the mixer up to high, continuing to beat until the mix forms stiff peaks. Repeat this step with the remaining granulated sugar until the whites are shiny and fluffy.

2 Sieve over the egg whites the icing sugar, almond flour, and matcha. Fold until they are just combined.

3 Preheat the oven to 150°C/300°F/Gas Mark 2 and line a baking sheet with paper.

4 Fill a piping bag with the macaron mix. Pipe 4 cm dollops onto the lined baking sheet and allow them to rest until they're no longer wet to the touch (allow up to one hour).

5 When the shells are dry, bake them for 15 minutes.

6 Take them out and leave them to rest when baked (for 10 minutes or until cool), and use this time to make the filling. Mix the icing sugar, cream cheese and milk in a bowl until smooth, then transfer this mix to a fresh piping bag and set aside until the shells are ready to fill.

7 When the shells have cooled, pipe the cream cheese mixture onto one shell, then sandwich with another macaron shell. Tuck in!

WOODEN BROOMSTICKS
(Peanut Butter Pretzel Broomsticks)

INGREDIENTS

- 1 pack pretzel sticks
- 1 pack breadsticks
- 3 tbsp peanut butter
- string

Makes: Make as many breadsticks as are in the pack
Prep Time: 10 to 15 minutes

METHOD

1 Break your pretzel sticks in half and divide them into groups of about eight.

2 Dip the end of your breadstick in peanut butter so that it is sticky. Place the pretzel halves around the sticky end of the breadstick and tie with string (or similar) to ensure they have properly stuck.

3 Serve your broomsticks upside down in a jar, and enjoy!

Halloween Special
(Pumpkin Risotto)

Ingredients

- 400 g (14 oz) pumpkin
- olive oil
- 2 garlic cloves, crushed
- 25 g (1 oz) butter
- 200 g (7 oz) risotto rice
- 2 tsp ground cumin
- 1 litre (35.2 fl oz) hot vegetable stock
- 50 g (2 oz) grated parmesan
- pumpkin, to serve
- oregano leaves, for garnish

Makes: 4
Prep Time: 30 minutes
Cook Time: 1 hour

Turn the page for the method.

METHOD

1 Heat the oven to 180°C/350°F/Gas Mark 4.

2 Chop the pumpkin into small cubes (approx. 1.5 cm). Put the pumpkin on a baking tray and drizzle with some oil, then roast it for 30 minutes.

3 Make a start on the risotto while the pumpkin is roasting. Heat the butter and one tablespoon of oil over a medium heat in a pan. Add the garlic and allow it to soften a bit before adding the rice and cumin. Stir well for about a minute to coat the ingredients in the butter.

4 Add 120 ml (4.2 fl oz) of the stock and gently stir until it has all been absorbed by the rice. Continue to add the stock and stir until all of it has been used up – allow around 20 minutes for this.

5 Check the rice is cooked – if it needs a little longer, add a splash more stock and continue to cook. Once it's soft, add the grated cheese and roasted pumpkin and gently stir. Serve the risotto inside a deseeded pumpkin and garnish with fresh oregano leaves.

WINTER CONJURINGS
(Beef Lasagne)

INGREDIENTS

- 2 tbsp olive oil
- 750 g (25 oz) lean beef mince
- 90 g (3 oz) pack prosciutto
- 800 g (30 oz) passata
- 200 ml (7 fl oz) hot beef stock
- a little grated nutmeg
- salt and pepper, to taste
- 300 g (10.5 oz) pack fresh lasagne sheets
- 520 g (20 oz) white sauce
- 125 g (4.5 oz) ball mozzarella
- basil leaves, for garnish

Makes: 6 servings
Prep Time: 20 minutes
Cook Time: 1 hour, 40 minutes

Turn the page for the method.

METHOD

1 Begin by making the meat sauce. Heat the oil in a frying pan and cook the beef for about 10 minutes until browned all over (we recommened doing this in two batches). Finely chop four slices of prosciutto and stir it through the meat mixure.

2 Pour over the passata and beef stock, then add the nutmeg and season to taste. Bring the pan to the boil then allow it to simmer for 30 minutes or until the sauce looks rich.

3 Heat the oven to 180°C/350°F/Gas Mark 4. Lightly oil an overproof dish that's approx. 30 cm x 20 cm.

4 Spoon one-third of the meat sauce into the dish and cover with lasagne sheets. Drizzle about one-quarter of the white sauce over the lasagne sheets.

5 Repeat step four until you have three layers of pasta. Top the lasagne with the remaining white sauce until the pasta sheets are completely covered.

6 Tear the mozzarella into small strips and scatter it over the top.

7 Bake the lasagne for 45 minutes until the top is bubbling and lightly browned. Add fresh basil leaves to decorate, then serve.

Boo!
Bananas
(Banana Ghosts)

Ingredients

- 4 bananas
- 24 chocolate chips, regular and/or mini sized

Makes: 8
Prep Time: 10 minutes

Method

1 Peel the bananas and cut them in half.

2 Place the bananas cut side down onto a plate or wooden board, so they stand up.

3 Decorate the bananas to look like ghosts by using small chocolate chips for the eyes and slightly larger chocolate chips for the mouths.

BREAKFAST MIRACLE
(Pumpkin Pie Smoothie)

INGREDIENTS

Makes: 2 glasses
Prep Time: 10 minutes

- 1 frozen banana
- 120 g (4 oz) vanilla Greek yoghurt
- ¼ tsp ground cinnamon
- ¼ tsp pumpkin pie spice
- 120 ml (4.2 fl oz) skimmed milk
- 2 tbsp maple syrup
- 150 g (5 oz) pumpkin purée
- ice
- cinnamon sticks, for garnish
- mint leaves, for garnish

METHOD

1 Use a strong, powerful blender to make this smoothie.

2 Add all of the ingredients to the blender (except for the cinnamon sticks and mint leaves for garnish), in the order listed.

3 Blend the ingredients on a high setting until smooth. Add a little more milk to thin out the smoothie if it's too thick.

4 Pour the smoothie into the glass and garnish with cinnamon sticks and mint leaves. Enjoy!

SPELLBINDING SOUP
(Spinach Soup)

INGREDIENTS

- 25 g (1 oz) butter
- 1 bunch spring onions, chopped
- 1 garlic clove, minced
- 120 g (4 oz) leek, sliced
- 85 g (3 oz) celery, sliced
- 200 g (7 oz) potato, peeled and sliced
- 1 litre (35.2 fl oz) stock
- 400 g (14 oz) spinach
- salt and pepper, to taste
- half-fat crème fraîche, to serve

Makes: 4 bowls
Prep Time: 10 minutes
Cook Time: 30 to 35 minutes

METHOD

1 In a large saucepan, heat the butter and then add the spring onions, garlic, leek, celery and potato.

2 Gently stir then put the lid on. Leave the soup for 10 minutes to sweat, stirring a couple of times.

3 Pour in the stock and continue to cook for 10–15 minutes until the potatoes have softened.

4 Add the spinach and season. Cook until the spinach has wilted then use a hand blender to blitz to a smooth soup.

5 Serve with a tablespoon of crème fraîche. Enjoy!

Sweet Sorcery
(Pumpkin Pancakes)

Ingredients

- 250 g (9 oz) pumpkin
- 2 free-range eggs
- 3 tbsp light brown soft sugar
- 25 g (1 oz) butter, melted
- 125 g (4.5 oz) buttermilk
- 200 g (7 oz) plain flour
- 2½ tsp baking powder
- 1 tsp ground cinnamon
- ¼ tsp salt
- 1 tbsp sunflower oil
- maple syrup, to serve
- fresh blueberries, to serve

Makes: 4 servings
Prep Time: 20 minutes
Cook Time: 25 minutes

Turn the page for the method.

METHOD

1 Peel and deseed the pumpkin, then chop it into large chunks. Put the chopped pumpkin into a heatproof bowl, add one tablespoon of water and cover it with cling film, then microwave for 5–8 minutes on high or until really soft.

2 Drain the pumpkin and leave it to cool completely (if you're making these for breakfast, we recommend completing this step the night before).

3 Once the pumpkin has cooled, put it in a food processor with the remaining pancake ingredients (not including the oil, maple syrup or blueberries). Blend until the ingredients have combined into a smooth, thick batter. Transfer the pancake batter into a jug.

4 To keep your pancakes warm as you cook them, heat the oven to 140°C/280°F/Gas Mark 1 and pop a baking tray inside. As you make each batch, you can transfer the pancakes from your pan to the baking tray to keep them warm until you're ready to serve them.

5 Heat a knob of butter and drizzle of oil in a large frying pan. When the butter is foaming, swirl it around the pan and pour evenly sized amounts of batter into the pan – they will spread as they cook so leave some space between each pancake.

6 Cook the pancakes over a low-medium heat and don't touch them until bubbles begin to appear on the surface. Have a look underneath and flip them if they're golden. Cook for a further two minutes on the other side.

7 Once cooked, stack the pancakes, drizzle them with maple syrup and decorate with fresh blueberries.

FOREST FINDS
(Mushroom Risotto)

INGREDIENTS

- 1 tbsp dried porcini mushrooms
- 2 tbsp olive oil
- 1 onion, chopped
- 2 garlic cloves, finely chopped
- 225 g (8 oz) chestnut mushrooms, sliced
- 350 g (12.5 oz) arborio rice / risotto rice
- 150 ml (5.2 fl oz) dry white wine
- 1.2 litres (42.2 fl oz) vegetable stock
- 25 g (1 oz) butter
- salt and pepper, to taste
- parsley, for garnish

Makes: 4 bowls
Prep Time: 25 minutes
Cook Time: 30 minutes

METHOD

1 Soak the porcini mushrooms in hot water for 10 minutes then drain well. Set aside.

2 Heat the oil in a large pan and add the onion and garlic. Fry them for 2–3 minutes over a gentle heat until softened, then add the chestnut mushrooms and fry for another 2–3 minutes until browned.

3 Add the rice and stir until coated with the oil. Gently pour in the wine and stir it at a simmer until the liquid has been absorbed.

4 Add a ladleful of the vegetable stock and allow it to simmer, stirring again until the liquid has been absorbed. Continue to add the stock in this way until all of the liquid has been absorbed and the rice is plump.

5 Roughly chop the soaked porcini mushrooms and stir them into the risotto. Add the butter and some salt and pepper to taste, then continue to stir.

6 Serve the risotto with a sprig of parsley for garnish. You may also like to garnish it with freshly grated parmesan as well.

WIZARDS' HATS
(Biscuit Cones)

INGREDIENTS

- 30 g (1 oz) butter
- ¼ tsp vanilla extract
- 1 tbsp milk
- 60 g (2 oz) icing sugar
- red and blue food colouring
- sprinkles (of your choice!)
- 10 chocolate cones
- 10 plain round biscuits

Makes: 10
Prep Time: 25 minutes

METHOD

1 In a medium bowl, beat the butter until fluffy. Add the vanilla extract and milk slowly while continually beating.

2 Add the sugar and continue beating until blended completely. Add the food colour (red 2; blue 1) until desired colour.

3 Spread a little buttercream on the rim of the cones and place them upside down on the biscuits. Spread more buttercream around the base of the cone and add a small dollop on the pointed top.

4 Cover with sprinkles as you desire and enjoy! Store remaining hats in the fridge in a sealed container.

TANTALISING TAGLIATELLE
(Green Pesto Tagliatelle)

INGREDIENTS

- 400 g (14 oz) tagliatelle
- pinch of salt
- 120 g (4 oz) green pesto
- grated parmesan, for garnish
- 4 tbsp lightly toasted pine nuts, for garnish
- basil leaves, for garnish
- salt and pepper, to taste
- drizzle of extra-virgin olive oil, for garnish

Makes: 4
Cook Time: 10 minutes for dry pasta, 3 minutes for fresh pasta

METHOD

1 Cook the pasta according to the instructions in a large pan of lightly salted boiling water. Once cooked, drain the pasta and put it in a large mixing bowl.

2 Put the pesto in the pan and warm it through, then add the pasta back to the pan and coat it with the pesto.

3 Serve the pasta with grated parmesan and a sprinkling of toasted pine nuts, then garnish with the basil.

4 You can also season the dish with freshly ground black pepper and a drizzle of olive oil.

HIDDEN TREASURES
(Plum & Apple Crumble)

INGREDIENTS

Makes: 6
Prep Time: 20 minutes
Cook Time: 30 minutes

- 6 large plums
- 500 g (17.5 oz) Bramley apples
- 50 g (1.7 oz) caster sugar or light brown sugar
- 1 tsp ground cinnamon
- 175 g (6 oz) plain flour
- 125 g (4.5 oz) butter, chilled and in cubes
- 50 g (1.5 oz) rolled oats
- 75 g (2.5 oz) demerara sugar

METHOD

1 Preheat the oven to 200ºC/390ºF/Gas Mark 6. Halve and stone the plums, roughly chop them and pop them into a large pan. Peel and core the apples, roughly chop them then add them and the sugar to the pan, along with the cinnamon and five tablespoons of water. Cover the pan and heat the

contents gently until the apples are softening (allow approx. five minutes).

2   Empty the fruit into a shallow, ovenproof serving dish and set aside.

3   To make the crumble topping, put the flour into a bowl. With your fingers, rub in the butter until the mixture resembles breadcrumbs. Add the oats and demerara sugar and mix again, then scatter the crumble topping over the fruit.

4   Bake in the oven for 25–30 minutes or until the crumble is golden brown.

AUTUMNAL MAGIC
(Beef & Vegetable Stew)

INGREDIENTS

- 1 tbsp vegetable oil
- 1 tbsp butter
- 2 celery sticks, thickly sliced
- 1 onion, chopped
- 2 big carrots, halved lengthways and chunkily sliced
- 5 bay leaves
- 1 whole thyme sprig
- 2 tbsp plain flour
- 2 tbsp tomato purée
- 2 tbsp Worcestershire sauce
- 2 beef stock cubes, crumbled
- 600 ml (21.1 fl oz) hot water
- 850 g (30 oz) stewing beef
- pumpkin, to serve

Makes: 5
Prep Time: 20 minutes
Cook Time: 3 hours, 50 minutes

Turn the page for the method.

METHOD

1 Heat the oven to 160°C/320°F/Gas Mark 3 and put the kettle on ready for later.

2 Put one tablespoon of oil and the butter into a casserole dish. Add the celery, onion, carrots, bay leaves and whole sprig of thyme to the dish.

3 Soften the vegetables for 10 minutes. Stir in the flour until it doesn't look dusty within the dish, and add the tomato purée, Worcestershire sauce and beef stock.

4 Gradually add the hot water and stir, then carefully add in the beef and bring to a gentle simmer.

5 Cover the dish and put it in the oven for 2½ hours, then take off the lid and cook for a further 30 minutes to one hour until the meat is tender and the sauce has thickened.

6 For an authentic touch, why not serve your stew in a deseeded pumpkin!

WISHING BROWNIE
(Chocolate Raspberry Brownie)

INGREDIENTS

- 200 g (7 oz) dark chocolate, broken up
- 100 g (3.5 oz) milk chocolate, broken up
- 250 g (9 oz) salted butter
- 400 g (14 oz) soft light brown sugar
- 4 large free-range eggs
- 140 g (5 oz) plain flour
- 50 g (2 oz) cocoa powder
- 200 g (7 oz) raspberries
- raspberry leaves, for garnish

Makes: 15 squares
Prep Time: 10 to 15 minutes
Cook Time: 30 to 35 minutes

METHOD

1 Preheat the oven to 180ºC/360ºF/Gas Mark 4.

2 Line a baking tray (approx. 30 x 20 cm) with baking parchment.

3 Put the dark and milk chocolate, along with the butter and sugar into a pan and gently melt it. Stir occasionally with a wooden spoon and remove from the heat once it's all melted and combined.

4 Add the eggs, one by one, to the melted chocolate mixture, stirring as you add each egg. Sieve over the flour and cocoa powder and stir it in. Then stir in half of the raspberries.

5 Pour the mixture into the baking tray and add the remaining raspberries.

6 Bake on the middle shelf for 30 minutes (add an additional five minutes to the baking time if you prefer a firmer texture).

7 Leave the brownie to cool when you take it out of the oven, before slicing it into squares. Garnish with raspberry leaves.

EARTHY BROTH
(Creamy Mushroom Soup)

INGREDIENTS

- 1 tbsp of olive oil
- 1 onion, finely sliced
- 2 sticks of celery, finely sliced
- 3 cloves of garlic, finely sliced
- a few sprigs of parsley
- a few sprigs of thyme
- 600 g (21 oz) mixed mushrooms
- 1.5 litres (52.7 fl oz) chicken / vegetable stock
- salt and pepper, to taste
- 75 ml (2.5 fl oz) single cream
- rosemary, to serve
- thyme, to serve

Makes: 6 bowls
Prep Time: 15 minutes
Cook Time: 45 minutes

METHOD

1 Finely slice the vegetables. Pick the parsley and finely chop the stalks, then pick the thyme leaves.

2 Heat the oil in a large pan over a medium heat and add the onion, celery, garlic, parsley stalks, thyme leaves and mushrooms. Cook gently with the lid on until all of the ingredients have softened.

3 Spoon out four tablespoons of the mushrooms and set them aside for later.

4 Keep the pan over a medium heat and pour the stock into the pan, bringing it to the boil. Turn the heat down to low and allow it to simmer for 15 minutes.

5 Season with salt and pepper to taste. Pop the mixture in a blender or whizz with a hand blender until smooth.

6 Add the cream and bring the pan back to the boil, then turn off the heat.

7 Spoon the soup into bowls and garnish with the mushrooms that were set aside earlier, along with fresh rosemary and thyme.

WITCH'S TART
(Leek & Courgette Tarts)

INGREDIENTS

For the tart filling:

- 1 tbsp coconut oil
- 3 garlic cloves, finely chopped
- 2 large leeks, finely sliced
- 150 g (5.5 oz) cheddar, grated (plus extra for sprinkling)
- 1 free-range egg yolk
- 2 tbsp crème fraîche
- splash of balsamic vinegar
- salt and pepper, to taste
- 1 courgette, finely sliced
- ½ leek, cut into rings
- dill, to serve

For the polenta pastry:

- 150 g (5.5 oz) plain flour
- 40 g (1.5 oz) finely ground instant polenta
- 120 g (4 oz) chilled butter, chopped
- 2 tbsp coconut oil
- 1 free-range egg
- 1 tbsp cold water

Makes: 4
Prep Time: 30 minutes
Extra Time: 30 minutes to chill the pastry
Cook Time: 30 minutes

Turn the page for the method.

Method

1   Preheat the oven to 200ºC/390ºF/Gas Mark 6.

2   Finely slice the garlic and leeks and sauté them in coconut oil until softened. Set them aside. Grate the cheese into a bowl, add the egg yolk and crème fraîche then whisk them all together. Once mixed, stir in the leeks and garlic along with a splash of balsamic vinegar, and season with salt and pepper to taste.

3   Next, make the pastry. Put the flour, polenta, butter and two tablespoons of coconut oil into a food processor. Mix on a pulse setting or hand-mix the ingredients. Add the egg and then some cold water to turn it to a dough consistency. Wrap the pastry mix in cling film and chill it in the fridge for 30 minutes.

4   Divide the pastry into four, roll it out and line the loose-bottomed tart tins. Line the pastry with greaseproof paper then bake blind (using baking beans) for 10 minutes. Afterwards, remove the paper and baking beans and bake the tarts for a further five minutes.

5   Leave them to cool before adding the wet mixture. Top the tarts with five courgette disks and a ring of leek, a sprinkle of grated cheese and the fresh dill. Bake the tarts in the oven for 8–10 minutes or until they are golden and bubbling on top.

BITTER SWEET
(Blackberry Muffins)

INGREDIENTS

- 75 g (2.5 oz) unsalted butter
- 4 tbsp natural yoghurt
- 2 large free-range eggs
- 200 g (7 oz) self-raising flour
- 1 tsp baking powder
- 1 tsp ground cinnamon
- 100 g (3.5 oz) dark brown muscovado sugar
- 100 g (3.5 oz) blackberries, halved if large

Makes: 10
Prep Time: 10 minutes
Cook Time: 20 minutes

METHOD

1 Preheat the oven to 190°C/375°F/Gas Mark 5. Pop the paper muffin cases into a 10-hole muffin tin.

2 Melt the butter and leave it to cool, then beat in the yoghurt and eggs, adding the eggs one at a time.

3 In a separate bowl, sieve the flour with the baking powder and cinnamon. Mix in the sugar and break up any lumps. Slowly add the wet mix (eggs, butter and yoghurt) to the dry mix and fold them together. Add the blackberries and stir to combine, but be careful not to over-mix.

4 Spoon the cake batter into the paper cases so they're three-quarters full. Bake them in the oven for approx. 18–20 minutes or until they're well risen and golden brown (you can test they're fully baked with a skewer – bake a little longer if there's any residue on the skewer).

5 Allow the muffins to cool before eating. Enjoy!